# DONKEY

## A Christmas Nativity Story

### By Niki Davies

Edited by Alison Hedger

Suitable for children aged 4 to 7 years
Approximate duration 20 minutes

Suitable for large or small casts
Flexible part allocation

Suitable for schools and churches

**TEACHER'S BOOK with CD**

The CD has demonstration songs and backing tracks for rehearsals and performances

The separate play part is in the Pupil's Book GA11682

## Golden Apple Productions

part of The Music Sales Group

Published by
**Golden Apple Productions**
14-15 Berners Street, London W1T 3LJ, UK.

Exclusive Distributors:
**Music Sales Limited**
Distribution Centre, Newmarket Road, Bury St Edmunds, Suffolk IP33 3YB, UK.
**Music Sales Corporation**
257 Park Avenue South, New York, NY 10010, USA.
**Music Sales Pty Limited**
20 Resolution Drive, Caringbah, NSW 2229, Australia.

Order No. GA11671
ISBN 978-1-84449-602-0
This book © Copyright 2004 by Golden Apple Productions.

Unauthorised reproduction of any part of this publication by any means including
photocopying is an infringement of copyright.

A licence should be obtained from the publishers for performances of this work.

Illustrations by jox
Music processed by Camden Music
Cover design by Butterworth Design
Printed in the United Kingdom

www.musicsales.com

## Cast (where lots of parts are needed)

**Narrator(s)**
**Old Man**                  Alfie's owner
**Alfie the Donkey**
**Joseph**                   Speaking
**Group of Buyers**          Three to speak
**Mary**                     Speaking
**Shepherds**
**Angels**                   Three to speak
**Innkeeper**
**Three Kings**              Speaking

### Optional extra parts:
**Old Man's Family**
**Travellers**
**Innkeeper's Wife**
**Three Kings' Attendants**
**Animals in the stable**

## Cast (where only a few parts are needed)

**Alfie the Donkey**
**Joseph**
**Mary**
**Shepherd(s)**
**Angel(s)**
**Three Kings**

If you are using Pre-School children, dispense with spoken lines by incorporating them into the narration, which will be spoken by an adult.

## Costumes and Props

The costumes are as one would expect in a children's Nativity play. In particular though:
- Mary is dressed all in blue
- Alfie the Donkey is dressed all in brown (roll neck sweater, brown tights with perhaps a tail: pointed ears attached to an Alice band)

Few props are needed, although it is always good to have at least one toy lamb and three decorated containers for the Kings' gifts.

## Stage Directions

Stage directions have mostly been omitted leaving teachers free to interpret the story as they wish. Basically the entrances and exits and movements on stage follow the script. How much mime is included depends upon individual preferences.

# Donkey For Sale

*Cue: But one day he became so poor that he decided the only thing he could do was sell Alfie.*

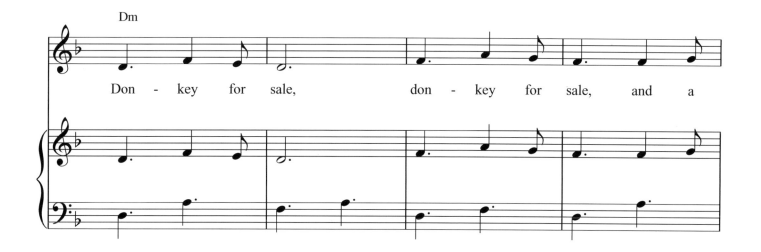

Don - key for sale, don - key for sale, and a

ve - ry fine don - key he is. Yes! A ve - ry fine

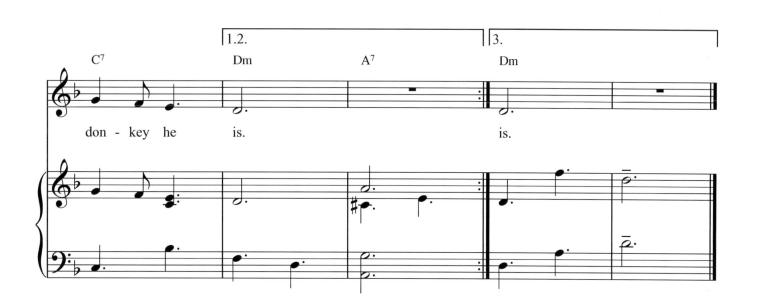

don - key he is. is.

5

# Pretty Lady In Blue

*Cue: Alfie thought she was the prettiest lady he had ever seen.*

# Just A Donkey

*Cue: They walked and walked and walked for days and days and days.*

**Chorus**

day.
are. } Clip, clip, clip, clop, lit - tle don - key, keep
day.

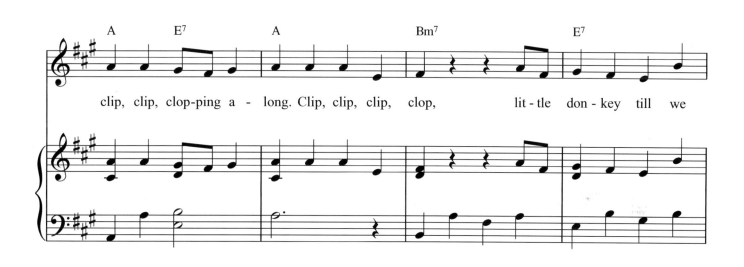

clip, clip, clop-ping a - long. Clip, clip, clip, clop, lit - tle don - key till we

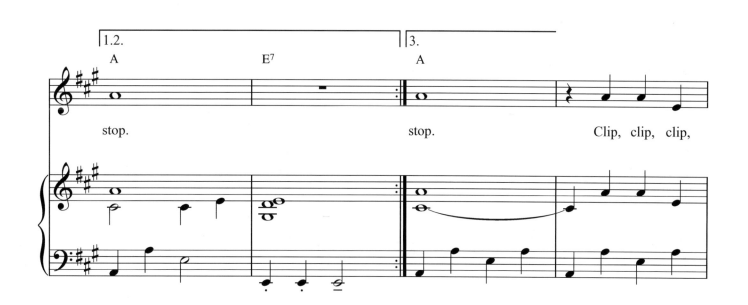

1.2.

stop.

3.

stop. Clip, clip, clip,

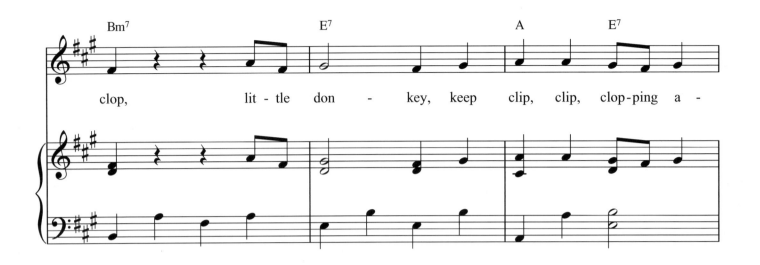

clop, lit - tle don - key, keep clip, clip, clop-ping a -

- long. Clip, clip, clip, clop, lit - tle don - key till we

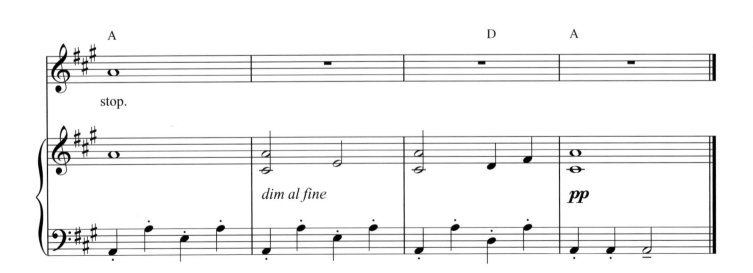

stop.

*dim al fine*

***pp***

# Hee-Haw

*Cue: But here he was, sold to two people who wanted him to walk and walk. He was very fed up!*

* For the hee-haws, you can mimic a donkey if you'd like.

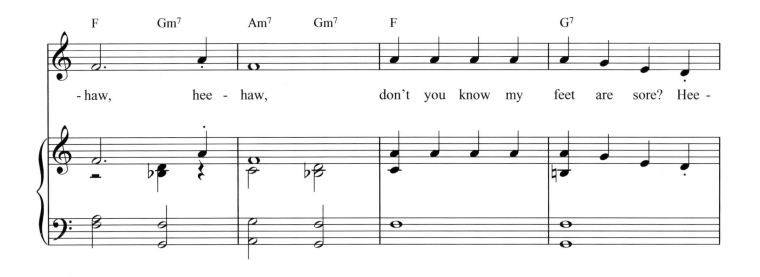

-haw,      hee - haw,      don't you know my    feet    are    sore? Hee -

**to Coda**

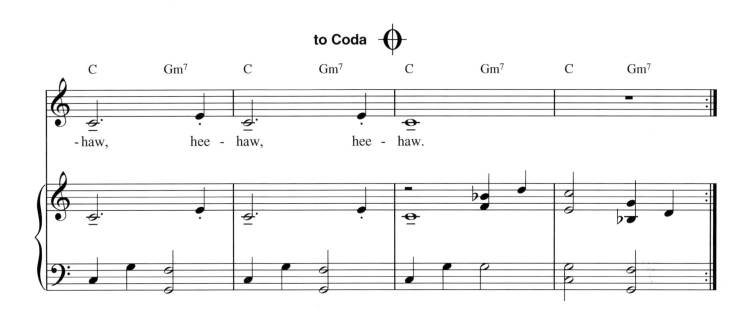

-haw,      hee - haw,      hee - haw.

**Instrumental**

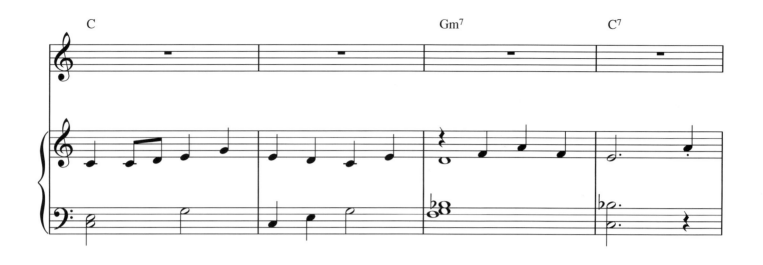

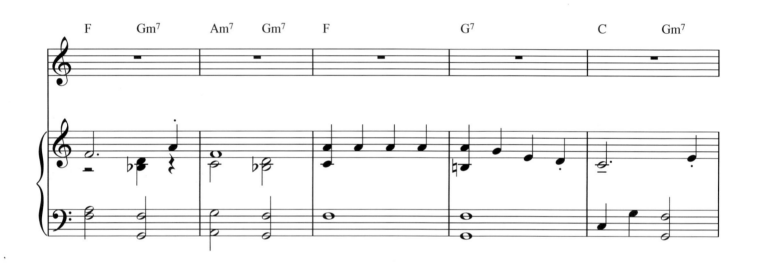

**D.S. al Coda**
(return to sing)

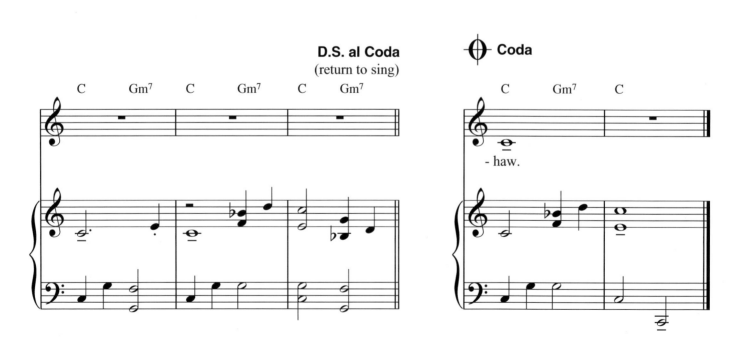

- haw.

# The Hill

*Cue: As they got closer, Alfie saw some angels hovering over the hill. It was such an amazing site.*

"Go to Beth - le - hem! Go to Beth - le - hem!

Go to Beth - le - hem to - night!"

- night!"

# Baby, Baby

*Cue: Lying in the manger was a little baby sleeping peacefully—a very beautiful and special baby, called Jesus.*

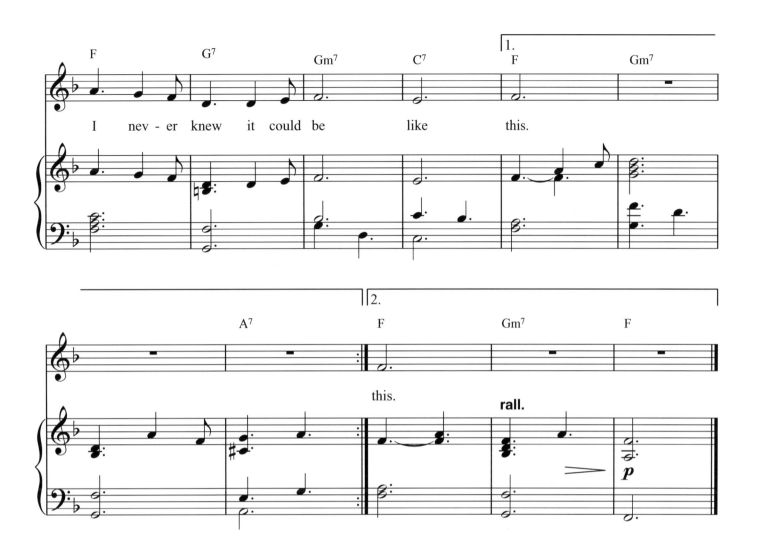

I nev - er knew it could be like this.

this.

rall.

21

# All To See The Tiny Child

*Cue: He was really glad to be there. And he wasn't fed up anymore!*

11/10 (176276)

## CD TRACK LISTING

**Full performances...**

1. **Donkey For Sale**
2. **Pretty Lady In Blue**
3. **Just A Donkey**
4. **Hee-Haw**
5. **The Hill**
6. **Baby, Baby**
7. **All To See The Tiny Child**

Vocals by Niki Davies
CD recorded, mixed and mastered by Neil Williams

**Backing tracks only...**

8. **Donkey For Sale**
9. **Pretty Lady In Blue**
10. **Just A Donkey**
11. **Hee-Haw**
12. **The Hill**
13. **Baby, Baby**
14. **All To See The Tiny Child**

To remove your CD from the plastic sleeve, lift the small lip on the side to break the perforated flap. Replace the disc after use for convenient storage.